# decades of

# the seventies

**Griffin House 161 Hammersmith Road London W6 8BS England**

Published 2001

**Editor:** Ulf Klenfeldt
**Cover Design:** Dominic Brookman
Special thanks to Howard Price,
EMI Music Publishing & Nathan Davidson, IMP

# decades of tv
## the seventies

### All Creatures Great And Small
One of BBC Television's most popular comedy drama series for many years, All Creatures Great And Small was based on the novels of James Herriot. Starting in 1936 and ending some time in the early 1950s, the stories chronicle the lives of the vets in a small practice in the Yorkshire Dales.

The first episode, entitled "Horse Sense", was aired on the 8th of January 1978. The show ran until 1990 and the final episode was called "Brotherly Love" and aired on the 20th of December 1990. In total there were 90 episodes, including three specials.

### Charlie's Angels
Few TV series scream out "1970s!" better than Charlie's Angels. Created by Starsky and Hutch producers Aaron Spelling and Leonard Goldberg. The series followed three female detectives routinely dispatched on crime-busting missions by Charlie, an always-unseen wealthy benefactor heard only by speakerphone (the character was voiced by Dynasty star John Forsythe). The Angels, as Charlie deemed them, would be assisted every week by the gazillionaire's right-hand man, John Bosley (David Doyle), as they chased ne'er-do-wells popping up every place from beauty contests and health spas to dude ranches and women's prisons. Of course, this presented a weekly opportunity for the viewing public to get an eyeful of the three lead actresses' cleavage, since they would always manage to shed some of their clothes in the name of the law. This was enough to make Charlie's Angels one of the top-rated prime-time shows in '78 and '79. As for the Angels themselves, they were a constantly changing crew.

Playing the super-sophisticated Kelly Garrett, Jaclyn Smith was the one Angel who lasted for the show's entire five-year run. Her record was closely followed by another of the charter Angels, Kate Jackson, who played the intelligent Angel, Sabrina Duncan, for the show's first three seasons. And, then, of course, there's Farrah Fawcett. Fawcett became an international superstar with her role as the highly athletic Jill Munroe. Fawcett left the series after one season, only to return in guest shots over the remainder of its run on ABC. Fawcett's replacement was Max Factor modeling sensation Cheryl Ladd, who likewise became a star playing Jill Munroe's sister, Kris, for three seasons. Kate Jackson was also replaced, in 1979, by Shelley Hack, as Tiffany Welles, who was in turn replaced the next year by Tanya Roberts as Julie Rogers. Ultimately, the series ran for 114 episodes before being cancelled in 1981 and entering television history as one of the defining series of the era.

### Fawlty Towers
The origins of 'Fawlty Towers' go back to 1971 when the 'Monty Python Flying Circus' team were filming scenes for their television series in the Torbay area (of course, the fictional location of Fawlty Towers). They had been booked to stay at the Gleneagles Hotel, where the owner of the hotel had a profound impact on the Python's and the history of television comedy.
The name of the hotel owner was Donald Sinclair, and it is he who must be afforded the title "the real Basil Fawlty". The details of the encounter between the Python's and Donald Sinclair are now legendary, mistaking Eric Idle's bag for a bomb and complaining about the way Terry Gilliam used his knife and fork. All the Pythons except John Cleese transferred from the Gleneagles Hotel to the more agreeable Imperial Hotel. John Cleese remained to watch and observe this bizarre character, whose behaviour was a gift to a comedy writer such as John Cleese. He was later joined by his then wife Connie Booth, who could also see the comedy potential of this man.
John Cleese having finished with 'Monty Python' (for the moment at least) began to look around for another project to employ his creative talents. He was approached by Jimmy Gilbert at the BBC to write a series for them, and it seemed only natural that he should team up with his wife Connie Booth for his next project. Remembering their experiences in Torbay in 1971 , they decided to write a series about a hotel manager and the people who get in the way of the smooth running of the hotel, that annoying section of the general public who insist on staying at hotels.
So, in September 1975 Basil Fawlty appeared to the unsuspecting British public in a series of six episodes on the BBC. Besides hapless Spanish waiter Manuel, whose tenuous grasp of the English language was explained by the fact that 'he comes from Barcelona', the hotel staff comprised chambermaid Polly, the voice of sanity in the eye of the storm, and chef Terry (in the second series). Resident guests whose mere presence was a constant irritant to Basil were the permanently confused Major Gowen and the elderly Miss Tibbs and Miss Gatsby. Four years later, Basil returned for a second series and the last ever episode - "Basil The Rat" was aired in October 1979. This is probably one of the most enduring television comedies of all time, and repeats always seem to bring it high in the ratings.

### Grandstand
The BBC's front line sports programme has become a national institution. Saturday afternoons would not be the same without Grandstand for thousands of sports fans in the UK who continue to enjoy its mix of live action, interviews, pools information and complete results service. It's name unsurprisingly encapsulated the mission of this televisual behemoth, where the viewer could have the 'best seat in the house', namely his or her own armchair, where they could comfortably while away the hours of the afternoon, and not miss a sporting moment. Grandstand has been host to many memorable sporting events including The Grand National, Roger Bannister's four-minute mile, five nation's rugby union, the boat race, and the Olympics.

Des Lynam, Frank Bough, David Coleman, John Motson and Gary Lineker, to name but a few, have all enjoyed working on the programme, be it as the anchorman, pundit, commentator or as presenter of the infamous preview and review sub-prog, Football Focus. The programme continues to develop with features such as 'Around The Grounds' that details the team line-ups in the Carling Premiership. Its sister programme Sunday Grandstand also captures the highlights of the sporting calendar, because there is no rest day for sportsmen.

Grandstand's theme tune is so memorable, it seems inconceivable that it will ever change. This music is so well known that I can safely say everyone is able to whistle it with confidence. And as long as there's sport there will be Grandstand. And you don't need a ticket.

### Grange Hill
Grange Hill is about life in a large secondary school - 11-16 year old pupils - set somewhere on the edge of London. This innovative programme was first transmitted on 8th February 1978 and for 17 years has regularly topped the ratings for children's drama programmes. It is generally recognised as a key watershed in children's television production, being the first hard hitting socially aware drama series. As a result it was an instant success with its intended audience - regularly achieving over 8 million viewers. The programme is widely regarded not only for its popularity but for its ability to sensitively tackle contemporary social issues, from bullying to drug addiction. Since 1978, the programme has received various distinctions, including four academy awards for Best Children's Series. This combination of entertainment and social awareness has proved perennially popular as audience research has shown that Grange Hill is watched by 75% of all 8-11 year olds in Britain - with the programme now being watched by its third generation, this percentage is likely to be accurate for most of the twenty-something audience.

### The Last Of The Summer Wine
Three go mad in Yorkshire. A trio of pensioners behaving badly prove that you don't need your own teeth to be a delinquent. Since the 12th of November 1973, making it the longest-running British TV sit-com of all time. Including specials, there have been around 170 episodes. Every series is supposed to be the last. Of the three central characters, two have been with the show from the very start -- wry widower Clegg (Peter Sallis), the former manager of a Co-op furniture department, and the fearless, shameless, brainless Compo (Bill Owen). The original third man was Blamire (Michael Bates), a retired Royal Signals sergeant, but when Michael Bates was taken ill in 1976 (he died shortly afterwards), a new character was introduced in the form of ex-army signwriter Foggy Dewhurst (Brian Wilde). With his attention to military detail, Foggy planned their adventures over the next nine years until, when Brian Wilde wanted to leave, Foggy departed for the sunnier climes of Bridlington, having inherited his uncle's painted-egg business. Retired teacher Seymour Utterthwaite (Michael Aldridge) arrived to complete the trio, only to leave in 1990 when Brian Wilde returned to the fold. In 1997, Foggy was replaced again, this time by the gang's old school pal, Truly (Frank Thornton). It is a show which boasts the title of being the Queen's favourite programme -- she is said to video it when she goes abroad.

## Liver Birds

First aired in 1969, The Liver Birds showed the the trials and tribulations for two flat mates in Liverpool. The pilot episode was showed on the 14th of April 1969. The first series started on the 25th of August the same year and showed Beryl Hennessey (Polly James) who shares a flat in Huskisson Street, Liverpool with Dawn (Pauline Collins). When Dawn decides to move on, at the end of the first series, Beryl finds a new flatmate, Sandra Hutchinson (Nerys Hughes). At the end of series 4, Beryl gets married and Carol Boswell (Elizabeth Estensen) takes her place in the flat. The first nine series concentrated on the problems encountered by two young single women when dealing with boyfriends, work, parents and each other. The series ended with the episode "The Best Things In Life Are Not Free" on the 5th of January 1979. In 1996 the programme was revived, with Beryl and Sandra now both coping with the aftermath of failed marriages. There was a strange lapse in continuity which resulted in Carol's mother and brother becoming Beryl's mother and brother. The revival contained 7 new episodes, but was less than successful and no further programmes were made.

## M*A*S*H

It all started with a book written by Dr. Richard Hornberger as he sat waiting for patients at his offices in Bremen, Maine. Using the pseudonym Richard Hooker it was a fictional account of his years at the 8055 Mobile Army Surgical Hospital in Korea. He based Hawkeye on himself (though he said he never liked Alda's portrayal of the character). Hornberger wrote a number of books featuring the same characters but non were as successful as the first.
The movie rights to Dr. Hornberger's book were bought for $100,000 by Ingo Preminger and a screenplay was written by Ring Lardner Jr who had been blacklisted by Hollywood in the fifties. The film was directed by Robert Altman and starred Donald Sutherland as Hawkeye and Elliot Gould as Trapper John. The movie was released in the fall of 1970 when anti-Vietnam sentiment was high, and was an instant hit. Ring Lardner Jr won the Oscar for Best Screenplay and the film was nominated for Best Movie. Sally Kellerman also received a Best Actress nomination for her role as Hotlips.

It was William Self (the president of Twentieth Century Fox) who turned the movie into a television series. With the movie set still available and with Fox owning the rights to the story he knew the series would be inexpensive to produce. The role of Hawkeye was the last character to be cast, apparently Alan Alda was reluctant to commit to a show that could have a long run.
The series lasted 11 years with 251 episodes made. It won countless awards and the final show was one of the most watched television program's ever.

## Pot Black

It was not until the late 1960s that colour TV broadcasting was introduced in the UK, and this was crucial to the development of snooker as a mainstream sport. The BBC had tried broadcasting snooker on the radio but this didn't really work out, they even tried showing games in black and white, but there were obvious drawbacks here.

There was little interest from the general public towards snooker on television, but despite this a programme was made featuring professional players playing each other in single frame matches on a weekly basis. This programme was Pot Black and it was first showed in 1969. It went on to become one of BBC2's most popular programmes.

## Starsky & Hutch

In September 1975 "Starsky and Hutch" premiered on television. In the 25 years since then, the pair of unorthodox, streetwise cops and their souped up hot rod Torino have become icons of disco style and violent-but-blood-free television. Just a few notes of the "wakka-chicka" theme song is enough to transport any child of the 70's back to those evenings parked in front of the tube. "Starsky and Hutch" ran for four seasons, a total of 88 episodes, including four special two-hour blocks. In those 92 hours David Soul and Paul Michael Glaser were called upon to shoot and be shot, squeal tires, impersonate salesmen, mobsters and Laurel and Hardy, laugh, cry, tell horrible jokes, sing, dance, support and insult, punch and hug each other. Though often hampered by too-hip dialog and lack of continuity, the humor and the humaness of the stories drew us in. Although the visual and verbal styles today seem laughably dated, the plots and characters were well crafted enough to stand up to the decades.

## Tales Of The Unexpected

This show was one of those overnight successes. Its creator Roald Dahl in fact hosted the first show broadcast in 1979. The master storyteller continued to weave his magic for the next nine years. Each story would have an unexpected twist to it, and the viewer was never quite sure what was going to happen next. This was a prime time hit for Anglia television.

The most popular memory for many will be the dancing lady in the opening titles. Her gyrating dance moves and outrageous arm flailing became as important to the viewer as the show itself. Many people still believe to this day that they were watching a naked female form, albeit as a silhouette, but those rumours can be quashed, since she was in fact wearing an all over body stocking. But now you too can dance to the actual theme tune, in the same style as the mysterious lady if you're that way inclined.

## Terry & June

Terry Medford (Terry Scott) and his wife June (June Whitfield) move to a new house in Purley, Surrey. June just wants a quiet life, but Terry has a knack for getting into difficulties and causing problems. Other regular characters include Terry's work colleague, Malcolm (Terence Alexander), his wife Beattie (Rosemary Frankau) and his boss, Sir Dennis Hodge (Reginald Marsh). The part of Malcolm was later played by Tim Barrett, then by John Quayle. In spite of the change of title and character names, this sitcom was basically a continuation of the earlier Happy Ever After. The first episode, entitled Long Weekend , was aired in October 1979 and the series ran for nine seasons, totalling 65 episodes

## Top Cat

Top Cat ("T.C." to his friends) is a sly con artist and the leader of a group of Broadway alley cats who live among Manhattan's overflowing trash cans --furnished with all the comforts of home! Despite the constant threat of eviction by Officer Dibble, T.C. and the gang enjoy a carefree existence as they plot their latest get-rich-scheme. Many of the characters and plotlines were inspired by the Phil Silvers sitcom "You'll Never Get Rich." Top Cat was Hanna-Barbera's 2nd prime time animated series (after The Flintstones), and debuted in the US on ABC in September 1961. 30 episodes were produced.

## The Waltons

Life in the South during the Depression was the subject of The Waltons. John and Olivia Walton and their seven children all lived together on Walton's Mountain, in the Blue Ridge Mountains of rural Jefferson County, Virginia. The family's modest income came from the lumber mill run by John and Grandpa Zeb. It was a close-knit family, with everyone helping out most of the time. There was no sex, no violence, just a warm family drama. Everything was seen through the eyes of John Boy, the oldest son, who had wanted to be a novelist for as long as he could remember.

It first appeared on the screen in 1972 and ended in 1981 totalling 221 episodes.

## The Wombles

It was back in 1968 that south Londoner Elisabeth Berseford began writing the first story of The Wombles. Her inspiration was drawn from her children, Kate and Marcus, who had difficulty with the pronunciation of Wimbledon Common, upon which they were walking. It was in fact Marcus upon whom she based her first Womble, namely Orinocco.

The Wombles could be described as rat-like creatures that dwelled in burrows under the Common. Their main purpose seemed to be 'making good use of the things that they found' on the Common, and turning whatever they found into (amongst other things) strange machines, largely with the help of Tobermory, the fix-it man, who'd give the A-Team a run for their money. The other Wombles were Great Uncle Bulgaria (the leader), Madame Cholet (the cook), Orinoco, Thomsk, Wellington, Adelaide and Bungo.

With hindsight it seems the underpinning 'green' message was well ahead of its time, with the need to recycle these days obviously paramount. These cuddly stuffed legends of children's television will always be remembered, together with it's sing-a-long theme tune

# All Creatures Great And Small

Music by Johnny Pearson

E7
A7
F♯7
Bm
B♭+
f
ff
D/A
E7/G♯
A11
1
2
(Da Capo)
A7
A
f
D/A
A11
D/A
A11
D/A
A11
D/A
f
D/A
A11
D/A
A11
D/A
A11
D

mf
D
G
F♯
B7
G
E7/G♯
A7
f
D/A
A11
D/A
A11
D/A
A11
D
D/A
A11
D/A
A11
D/A
A11
D
mf
D
G
E
A

f
F♯
Bm
Bm7/A
Em7/G
G♯°
ff
D
r.h.
A7
f
D
G6/D
D
G/D
D
A7/D
D
D/A
A11
D
A11
D/A
A11
r.h.
rall.
D
G
D
G
D

# Charlie's Angels

Music by Allyn Ferguson and Jack Elliott

Dmaj7
Bm7
Gmaj7
Em7
6
6
Em9
Cmaj7
Am7
3
Emaj9

# Fawlty Towers

Music by Dennis Wilson

D
Bm
E7
G♯dim
Am
B♭dim
G
Gdim
2fr
G
G♯dim
Am7
D7
to Coda ⊕
1.
G
2.
G
G
D11
D9
3fr
G
D11
D9
3fr
G
D.𝄋 al Coda
⊕ CODA
G

# Grandstand

Music by Keith Mansfield

C/G
G
G/A
A
G/A
A
B7♭9
Em7
A7
Dmaj7
Gmaj7
C♯m7
F♯7
Bm
B7♭9
Em7
A7
F♯7
Bm
G
D/F♯
G/A
N.C.
G
D/F♯
to Coda ⊕
Em7
F♯m
G
D
G/D
D
G/D
D

G/D
D
A
D/A
Instrumental solo
B
E/B
C#
4fr
F#/C#
D.𝄋 al Coda
CODA
Em7
F#m
G
3fr
C
N.C.

# Gotcha (Starsky & Hutch)

Music by Tom Scott

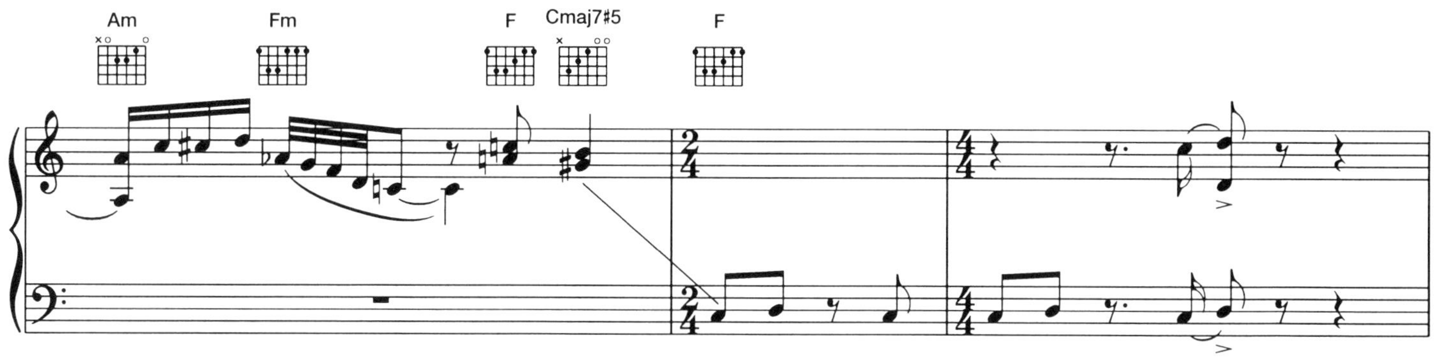


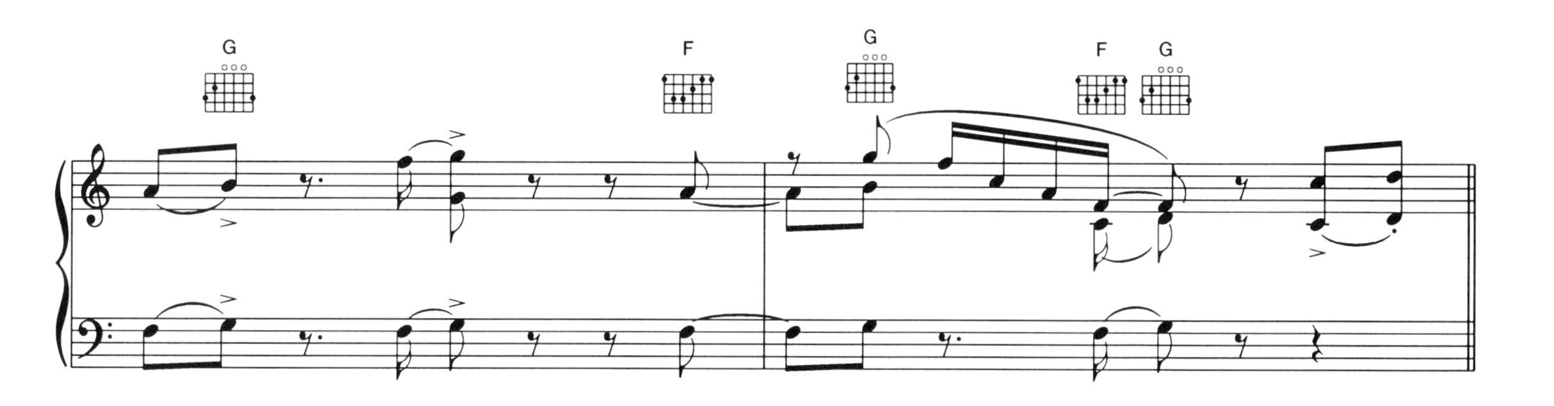


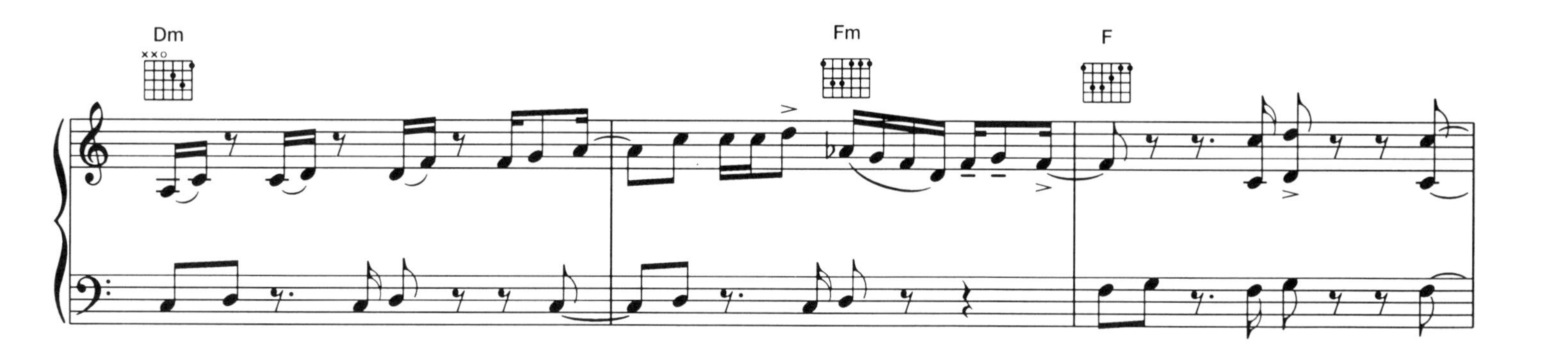

Dm
Fm
F
Dm
Fm
F
Am
D
Am
D
Am

Am
B♭
G
C
F
G
F
G
F
G
Dm
Fm
F
D.C. al Coda
to Coda
CODA
Am
Am
Fm
F
Dm

# Chicken Man (Grange Hill)

Music by Alan Hawkshaw

G7
B♭maj7
A7aug
Dm
Dm6
B♭
A7
N.C.

# The Last Of The Summer Wine

Music by Ronnie Hazlehurst

to Coda ⊕
F/C
G7/C
C
F
Em
Dm7
G7
C
Fm7
D.𝄋 al Coda
E♭
A♭6/E♭
Fm6/D
G11
G
⊕ CODA
G7/C
C
A♭
D♭9
G♭
F

# Liver Birds

Traditional arranged by Cecil Bolton

F
C
F
E♭
E♭maj7
E♭7
E♭6
E♭aug
E♭
E♭6
E♭maj7
E♭
E♭/D
E♭/D♭
C9
f
Fm7
B♭7
E♭
E♭maj7
E♭6
E♭7
E♭aug
E♭
E♭6
E♭maj7
E♭
E7
Fm7
G7aug
C9
Fm7
B♭11
B♭7
E♭
Fm/E♭
E♭
Fm7add4/B♭
E♭
Fm/E♭
E♭
mf
p

# Suicide Is Painless (Theme From M*A*S*H)

Words by Mike Altman
Music by Johnny Mandel

2. Try to find a way to make
   All our little joys relate
   Without that ever present hate
   But now I know that it's too late
   And, *Chorus*

3. The game of life is hard to play
   I'm going to lose it anyway
   The losing card I'll someday lay
   So this is all I have to say
   That: *Chorus*

4. The only way to win, is cheat
   And lay it down before I'm beat
   And to another give a seat
   For that's the only painless feat
   'Cause; *Chorus*

5. The sword of time will pierce our skins
   It doesn't hurt when it begins
   But as it works it's way on in
   The pain grows stronger, watch it grin
   For: *Chorus*

6. A brace man once requested me
   To answer questions that are key
   Is it to be or not to be
   And I replied; "Oh why ask me?"
   'Cause: *Chorus*

Tales Of The Unexpected
Music by Ron Grainer
Bright Waltz Tempo (♩. = 62)
mf
Ab
Abmaj7
Ab6
Abmaj7
Ab
Abmaj7
Ab6
Ab
Bbm
Bbm6
Bbm7
Ab
Abmaj7
Ab6
Ab
Bbm7
Bbm6
Eb7

A♭
4fr
B♭m
A♭
4fr
B♭m7
E♭7
A♭
4fr
E♭
A♭
4fr
1.
2.
A♭
4fr

B♭m7
E♭7
f
A♭maj7
3fr
A♭6
4fr
Fmaj7
B♭m7/E♭
F7
B♭m7
B♭m7♭5
E♭7
N.C.
B♭m7
A♭
4fr

B♭m7
E♭7
A♭
4fr
E♭
A♭
4fr
B♭m
B♭m6
B♭m7
A♭
4fr
A♭maj7
3fr
A♭6
4fr
A♭
4fr
B♭m7
E♭7
A♭
4fr
E♭
A♭
4fr

# Black And White Rag (Pot Black)

Music by George Botsford

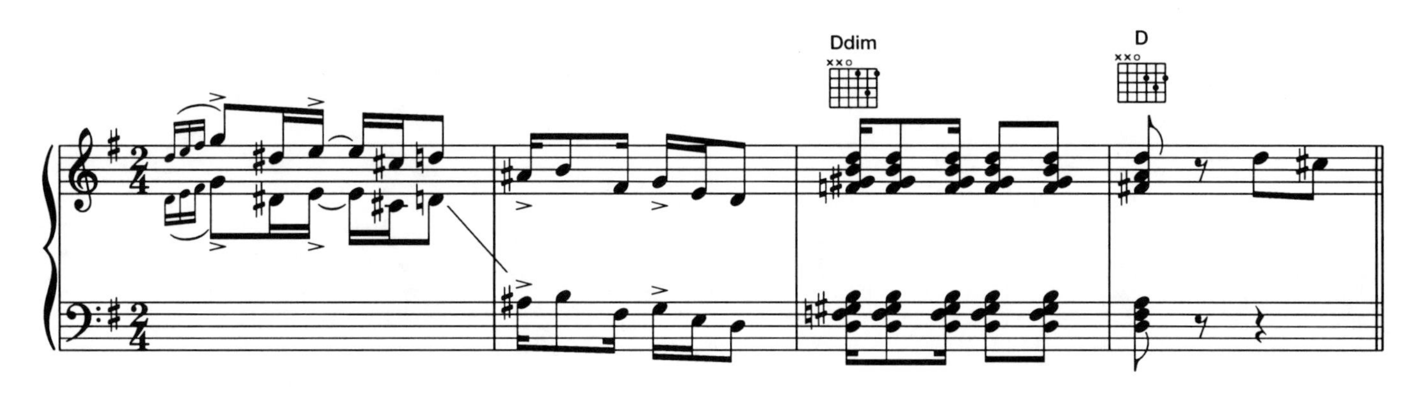


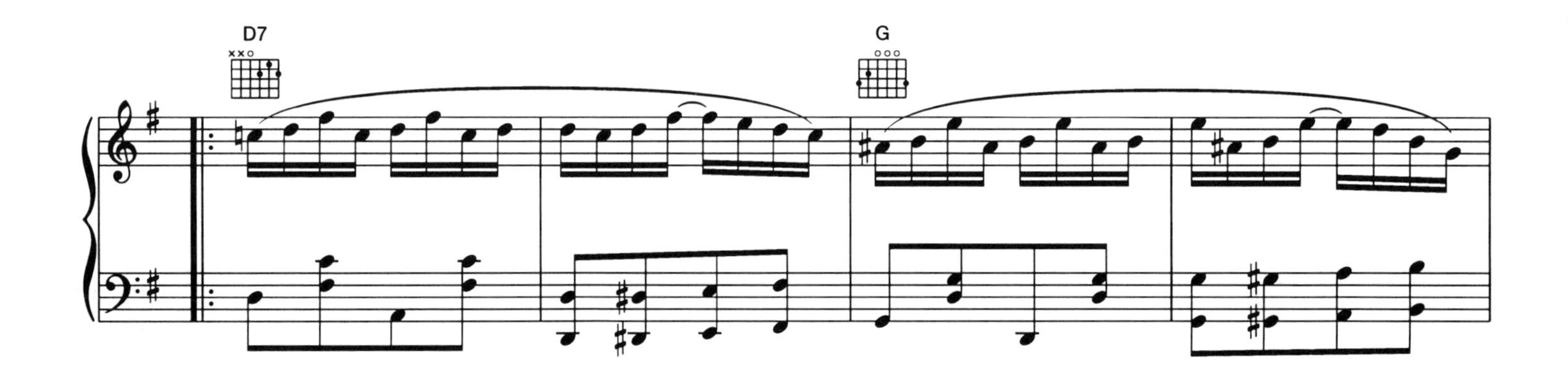


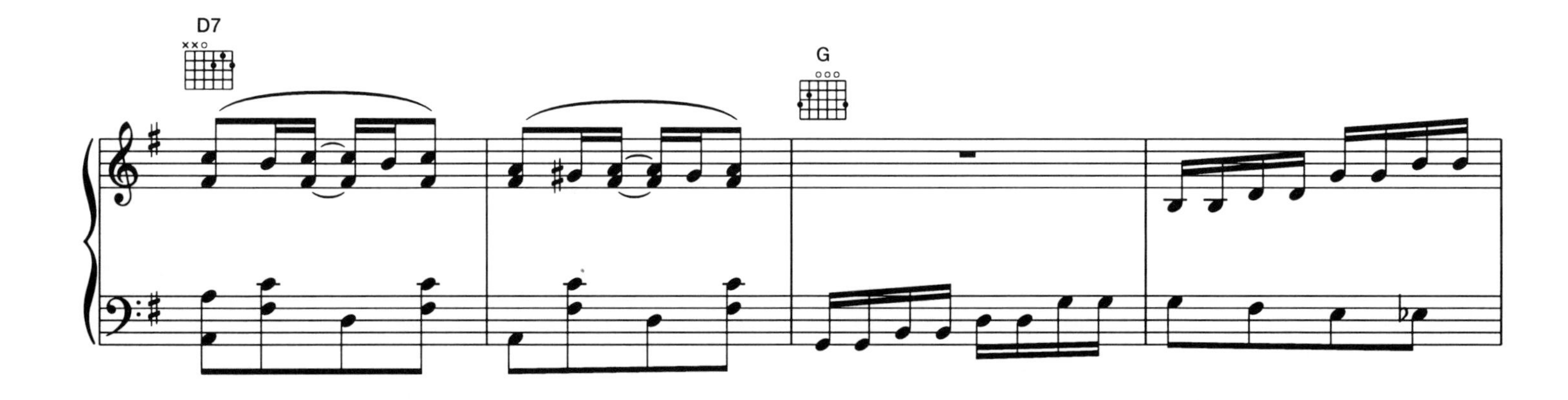


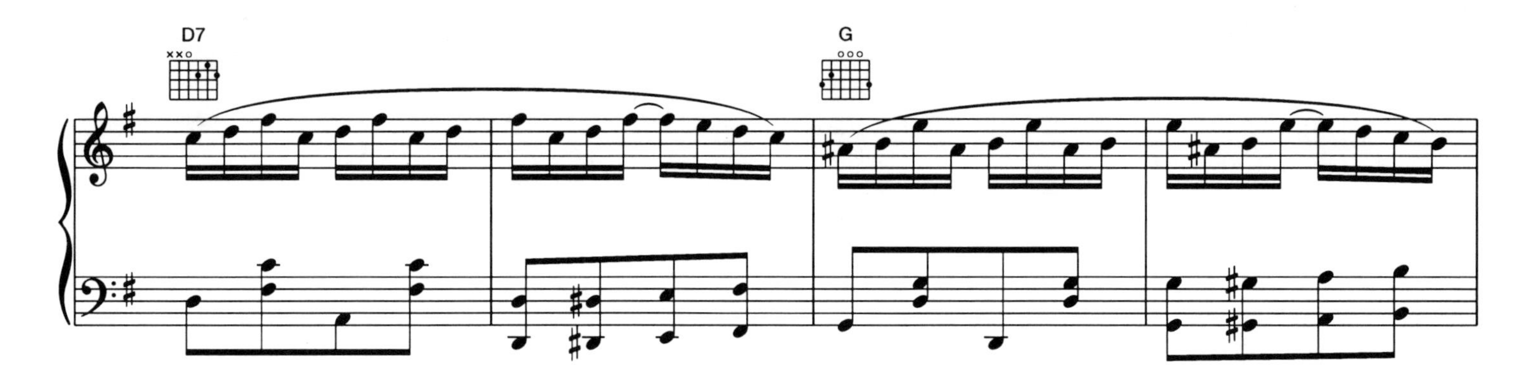

E7
Am
G
D7
1.
G
2.
G
G
D7
G
E7
Am

G
D7
1.
G
2.
G
D7
G
D7
G
D7
G

E7
Am
G
D7
G
Fine
C
D7
G
C
D7
G

1.
2.
C
G
D7
G7
C
C
C
G7
C
A7
Dm
C
G7
C
D.C. al Fine

# Bell Hop (Terry & June)

Music by John Shakespeare
and Joan Shakespeare

# Top Cat

Words and Music by
William Hanna and Joseph Barbera

F7
B♭6
Gm7
Cm7
F7
with dig - ni - ty.
Top Cat,
the in - dis - put - a - ble
B♭
B♭7
E♭6
Edim7
lead - er of the gang.
He's the boss, he's a wit, he's a
B♭/F
G7
C9
F7
B♭6
num - ber one VIP.
He's the most tip top,
Top Cat.
E♭/F
A6
B♭6
Gm7

Cm7
F7
B♭6
B♭9
E♭6
Yes, _ he's the
Edim7
B♭/F
G7
C9
chief, he's the king, but a - bove ev - 'ry - thing, _ he's the most tip top,
F7
B♭6
B♭6
E♭7
A♭7
D♭7
B♭6
Top Cat.
*Top Cat!*

# The Waltons

Music by Jerry Goldsmith

2.
D
G
C
G
Fine
G7
C
F
C
f
G
B♭
G
F
D7
D
G
C
G

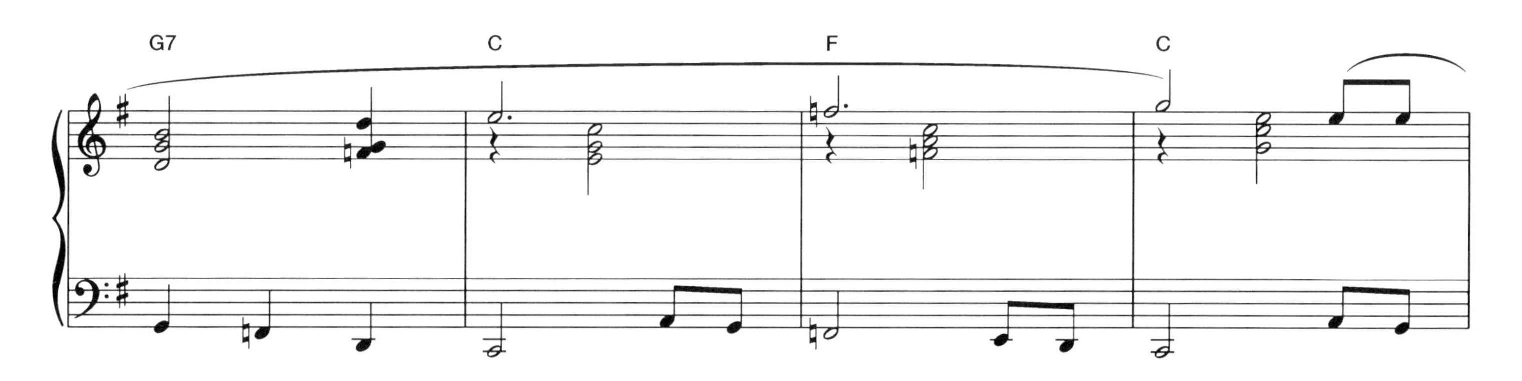
G7
C
F
C

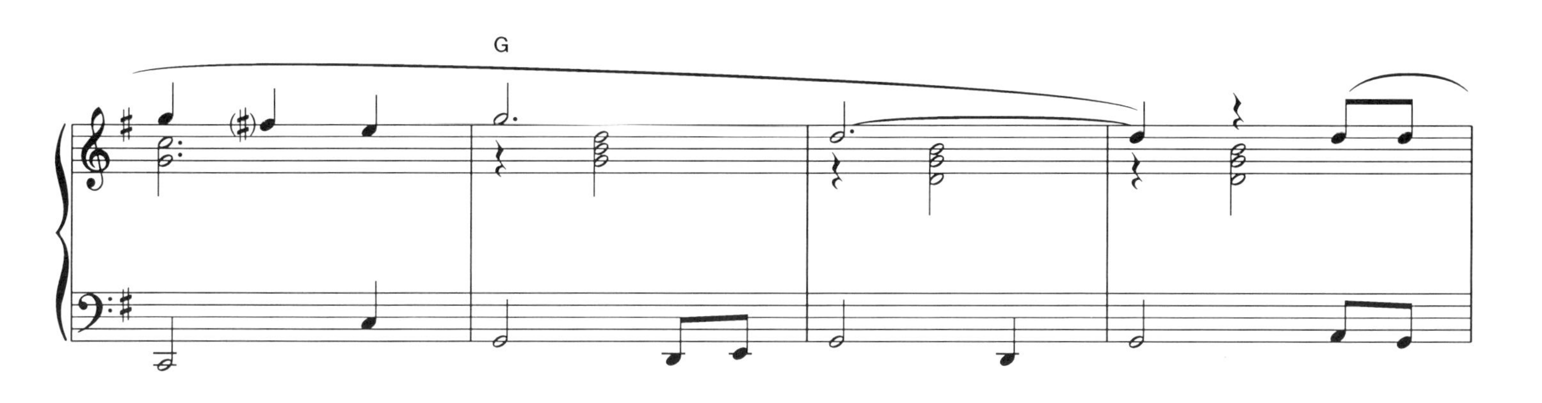
G

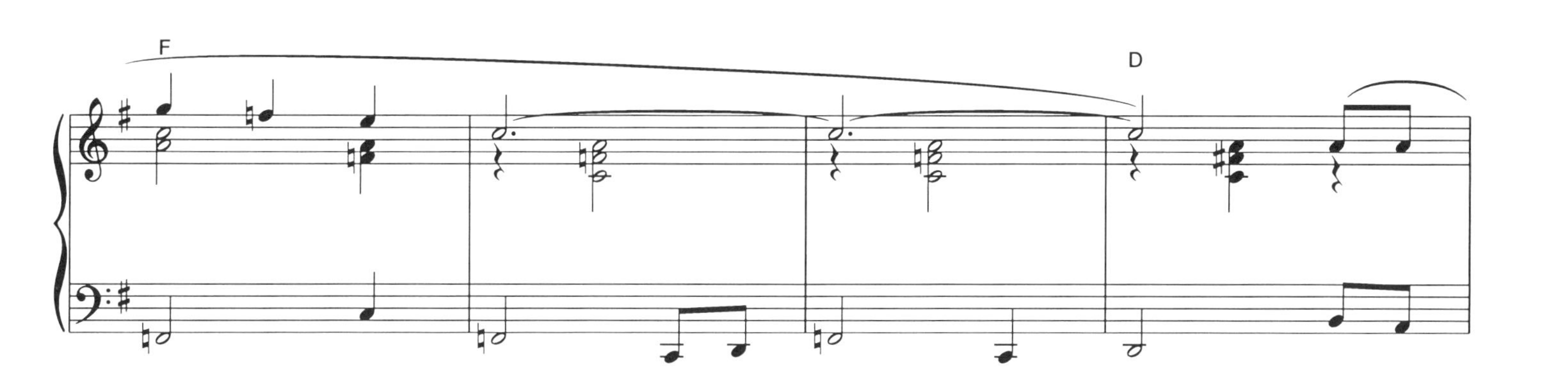
F
D

G
C
rit.
G
D.𝄋 al Fine
Tempo I

# The Wombling Song

Words and Music by Mike Batt

Am D G Gmaj7 Em G
- mon are we. Mak - ing good use of the things that we find,
C G Am D E E7
things that the ev - ery-day folks leave be - hind. Un - cle Bul - ga - ri-a, he can re - mem -
Am Am7 D G
- ber the days when he was - n't be - hind "The Times" with his
B7 Em Em7 C
map of the world, pick up the pa - pers and take 'em to To - ber-mo - ry.

People don't notice us, they never see
Under their noses a Womble may be
We Womble by night and we Womble by day
Looking for litter to trundle away

We're so incredibly utterly devious
Making the most of everything
Even bottle and tins
Pick up the pieces and make 'em into something new

Underground, overground, Wombling free
The Wombles of Wimbledon Common are we
Making good use of the things that we find
Things that the everyday folks leave behind

Printed and bound in Great Britain 2/01